Happily Ever After

Ian Serraillier

POEMS FOR CHILDREN

Happily Ever After

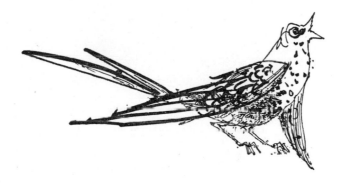

Illustrated by

BRIAN WILDSMITH

London
OXFORD UNIVERSITY PRESS
1963

Oxford University Press, Amen House, London E.C. 4

GLASGOW NEW YORK TORONTO MELBOURNE WELLINGTON
BOMBAY CALCUTTA MADRAS KARACHI LAHORE DACCA
CAPE TOWN SALISBURY NAIROBI IBADAN ACCRA
KUALA LUMPUR HONG KONG

First published 1963

Printed in Great Britain by
W. & J. Mackay & Co Ltd, Chatham

TO

My Family and Friends

Acknowledgements

Acknowledgement is made to Heinemann Educational Books Ltd. for permission to reprint *The Hedgehog* and *Swallows in the Beach Hut*, and to Faber and Faber Ltd. for permission to use *After Ever Happily*, *Too Polite* and *Your Poet*, which first appeared in VERSE THAT IS FUN, compiled by Barbara Ireson.

Contents

FAMILY AND FRIENDS

Your Poet   3

Grandad's Pipe   4

The Early Visitor   5

Anne and the Field-Mouse   8

What will you have for Breakfast?   10

The Hedgehog   13

The Swan   15

Andrew's Bedtime Story   16

Falling Asleep   18

AT THE SEA

The Diver   21

The Helicopter   22

Shrimping   23

Swallows in the Beach Hut   25

North-Easter   26

Hares and Hounds   28

STORIES

Too Polite 33

Piano Practice 34

Brewster Dick 35

  1 THE CHASE 35

  2 WHAT HAPPENED AFTERWARDS 37

The Witch's Cat 40

After Ever Happily 42

FAMILY AND FRIENDS

Your Poet

SCRIBBLING verse, my pencil gropes
Across the backs of envelopes,
And while I'm cumulating stock it
Bulges from my jacket pocket.

I sit indoors in rainy weather,
Cementing all the bits together;
Sometimes I get into a fix
And, when the bits don't fit, I stix.

Grandad's Pipe

AFTER tea, while others knit,
Two children, tired, excited, sit
On Grandad's knee as the pipe is lit.
    'I'm lighter-up!' said she.
    'I'm blower-out!' said he.

She strikes the match. When sparks are growing,
He blows it out with one great blowing,
And Grandad sucks till the pipe is glowing.
    'I'm lighter-up!' said she.
    'I'm blower-out!' said he.

The smoke climbs up in clouds of blue
To melt or pierce the ceiling through,
And all their troubles vanish too.
    'I'm lighter-up!' said she.
    'I'm blower-out!' said he.

The Early Visitor

Rat-tat-tat on the door! Six o'clock
Of a winter's morning;
And Lionel, Kit and Clare (that's me)
Tumble out of sleep,
Stretching, yawning,
Then shoot down the stairs
To ram back the bolts and open—
It's Mr. Knight, the sweep.

We show him the fire-place,
Its grimy vacant face
Gaping at the ghosts of chairs,
And watch him unshoulder his sack and fix
His backbone of sticks
With the golliwog's head on top,
Then lean into the chimney and cry,
'Up she goes!'

5

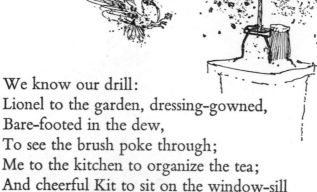

We know our drill:
Lionel to the garden, dressing-gowned,
Bare-footed in the dew,
To see the brush poke through;
Me to the kitchen to organize the tea;
And cheerful Kit to sit on the window-sill
With his bag of bull's eyes, and gaze and chew.
The rest of us go to it with a will.

The kettle starts to splutter
As a voice from the garden sings shrill,
'Hurrah, the brush is through!
Snowballs of soot
Are spilling into the gutter!'
Lionel runs in, his heart a-flutter,
And the cock over the wall crows,
'Cock-a-doodle-doo!'

I'm back with my tray of tea and find
The deed is done:
A bucket of soot on the hearth beside
Half another one—nothing dirty,
Not a speck on the floor, and the ghosts
In the electric light
As scrubbed-and-laundered white
As a bridal party.

And while we're drinking,
I know what Lionel's thinking:
There's no one in the world like Mr. Knight.
And cheerful Kit: *God knows, I could sit here watching*
Him all day, till the factory whistle blows.
And me: *I'd marry him any time, keep house*
And make his morning cuppa,
Wash and iron his jeans and cook his supper.

He mounts his bicycle, and away he goes
With his sticks and golliwog's head and sack
Into the misty morning. We hope
He'll soon be back . . .
Tiptoe upstairs to dress,
Past the parents' door—can you hear them snoring,
Oblivious of our bliss?
How boring, and think what they miss!

Anne and the Field-Mouse

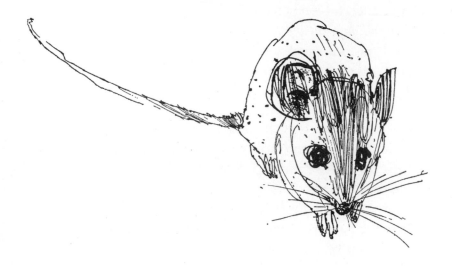

WE found a mouse in the chalk quarry today
In a circle of stones and empty oil drums
By the fag ends of a fire. There had been
A picnic there; he must have been after the crumbs.

Jane saw him first, a flicker of brown fur
In and out of the charred wood and chalk-white.
I saw him last, but not till we'd turned up
Every stone and surprised him into flight,

Though not far—little zigzag spurts from stone
To stone. Once, as he lurked in his hiding-place,
I saw his beady eyes uplifted to mine.
I'd never seen such terror in so small a face.

I watched, amazed and guilty. Beside us suddenly
A heavy pheasant whirred up from the ground,
Scaring us all; and, before we knew it, the mouse
Had broken cover, skimming away without a sound,

Melting into the nettles. We didn't go
Till I'd chalked in capitals on a rusty can:
THERE'S A MOUSE IN THOSE NETTLES. LEAVE
HIM ALONE. NOVEMBER 15th. ANNE.

What will you have for Breakfast ?

A PLEASANT boy was Richard, but
  While staying with a friend
Named Andrew M., the only son
  Of Mr. Round-the-Bend,
He met a most regrettable
  And melancholy end.

It was while they sat at breakfast that
  Young Richard burnt his boats
By asking for a helping of
  Old-fashioned porridge oats.
(Such stodge would be despised by self-
  Respecting nanny-goats).

A fancy so astonishing
    They could not but refuse,
And pointing to the cereals
    They asked the boy to choose.

That gaudy cardboard multitude
    Bewildered the poor guest;
He asked the Round-the-Bends in turn
    Which one they liked the best.

'The blue for me,' said Mrs. R.,
    'I buy it by the sheaf.
I'm fond of beads and necklaces
    And brooch of clover-leaf.'

Andrew favoured red: 'I thrive
    On plastic puzzle toys,
As submarines and aeroplanes
And trucks and Continental trains
    Are good for growing boys.'

'I find,' said Mr. Round-the-Bend,
    'The yellow one's my fate.
There's seldom anything left except
    For Peerless Silver Plate.'
'And serves you right,' said Mrs. R.,
    'You always get up late.'

'How do you take it?' Richard asked.
    He said, 'I take it neat.
It's good for indigestion and
    It helps to warm my feet.'

Young Richard, though confused by such
    No doubt well-meant advice,
Was never inconsiderate:
    'This cheaper one looks nice—
A kit of tools in stainless steel
    Offered at half the price.'

When he'd turned out all the packing (lots
    Of bloated candy puff),
There was nothing there to eat—you had
    To send up for the stuff.

The boy was dreadfully upset.
    'They've cheated me!' he cried.
'Not a bite to eat since yesterday—
    My stomach's gaping wide!'
And, swallowing *all* the packing, most
    Unhappily he died.

The Hedgehog

THERE's a hedgehog in the garden—come and see.
When he's still, he's like a pincushion that breathes.
When he moves, he's like a fat freckled mouse, following
   me
All over the place with pitter-patter feet.
He snorts and snuffs and sniffs my shoe,
Then hauls himself over the rise.

We'll introduce him to the cat. But she runs away
Into the box-tree, all hidden save her eyes
And nose and twitching tail—
Then suddenly leaps out and pounces.
(Can you blame her? He's drunk all
Her saucerful of milk, three fluid ounces.)

Caught?
Not likely. She pulls up short
And dances and prances and saws
The air all round him, mighty dainty with her paws;
Then, defeated, slinks away
To sulk or chase less prickly prey.

It's chilly now and getting late.
We'll cover him with a pile of autumn leaves
And let him hide or even hibernate.
In the morning we'll creep
Over the lawn and part the leaves and peer
Inside, and see if he's lying there asleep.
I hope he is . . .

He wasn't. He was out of his heap,
Waiting for me—wide awake perhaps all night?—
And came running towards me and round me and after
    me
All over the place with pitter-patter feet.

Now, were I the kind of poet
Who liked to preach
Of earth and man and animal bound each to each,
I'd draw the moral here: *We two, travellers together*
Hand in hand through life's journey
To an unknown end—would we could know it! . . .
Hand in hand? Ugh, those prickles! Thank you,
I prefer to keep my distance, to stay awhile,
To watch, enjoy my play awhile,
Then leave him to it.

The Swan

HE glides over the glassy pool
From cloud to cloud, serene and cool,
Choosing the fairest; poised to peck,
Plunges down his snowy neck.
And what were white and foaming fleeces
Shiver into shapeless pieces.

Andrew's Bedtime Story

I TOLD him a tale that I adore
Called *Theseus and the Minotaur*,
Of how a prince with a ball of wool
   That his girl friend Ariadne gave him,
Was forced to search for a fiery bull
   Through cave and labyrinth. Keen to save him,
She said, 'Unwind the wool as you go
Through the twisting corridors down below,
And return to me safe—I love you so.'

That was the start of the tale I told,
And Andrew listened, as good as gold.

Next day when he ran home from school,
He found a skein of his mother's wool,
Unwound it, tied it to door and chair,
Along the passage and up the stair,
    Yes, everywhere.
  I opened the door of my room
      To find
Pitschi the cat with his legs entwined,
Jane and Helen flat on the floor,

Great-aunt almost sliced at the knees
(As wire at the grocer's slices cheese),
    All of them trapped.
    The thread I snapped,
With scissors and knife I hacked away
    And set them free.
    But where was A?
There, in a corner lurking, laughing.
    'No more
    Of Ariadne's thread,
My boy,' I cried, 'or we'll all be dead!'
    I stalked away.

But a murderous thread not seen before
Tripped me up, and I cracked my head.

Falling Asleep

I CAN'T fall asleep
When Mummy goes to choir. I've said
My prayers, the cat is purring on my bed,
And Daddy's reading downstairs. My head
  Lies pillowed deep,
  But I can't fall asleep,

  I can't fall asleep
Or settle. Though Mummy has undressed me
And bathed me and bedded me and kissed me,
I wonder—while she's singing—has she missed me?
  Will I never fall asleep?
  The long hours creep,

  The long hours creep
So slowly . . . Then at last the front door
Bangs, and I hear her cross the floor.
I call good night and she kisses me once more
  And hugs me. I could weep
  For joy. But I fall asleep.

AT THE SEA

The Diver

I PUT on my aqua-lung and plunge,
Exploring, like a ship with a glass keel,
The secrets of the deep. Along my lazy road
On and on I steal—
Over waving bushes which at a touch explode
Into shrimps, then closing rock to the tune of the tide;
Over crabs that vanish in puffs of sand.
Look, a string of pearls bubbling at my side
Breaks in my hand—
Those pearls were my breath! . . . Does that hollow
   hide
Some old Armada wreck in seaweed furled,
Crusted with barnacles, her cannon rusted,
The great *San Philip*? What bullion in her hold?
Pieces of eight, silver crowns, and bars of solid gold?

I shall never know. Too soon the clasping cold
Fastens on flesh and limb
And pulls me to the surface. Shivering, back I swim
To the beach, the noisy crowds, the ordinary world.

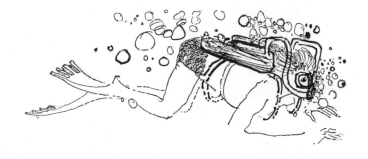

The Helicopter

ALONG the rim of sea and sky
  The helicopter roars,
Ready to hover low and scoop
  The drowning from our shores.

A cavern in the side reveals
  Perched on his windy seat
The rescuer, who waves to us
  And dangles both his feet.

Suppose he fell, on the page of sea
  Splashing, an inky blotch;
He'd have to save himself, and that
  Would be some fun to watch.

Shrimping

I TAKE my shrimping net, wade into the pool
Right up to my shins and push. The water's cool,
Rippling round my shins; from each sandy foot
Shrimps like flying splinters dart and shoot,

Then vanish into seaweed-swaying banks.
I chase behind, surprise them from the flanks,
Churning the weed above, the sand below,
Till my wooden handle's bent as an archer's bow.

I stagger to the edge to empty out my treasure,
The wonders of the deep, wave-wealth beyond measure:
Garlands, puffs frilled like a ballet skirt,
A bunch of jellied fingers to pinch and squirt,

Ribbons of brown satin, sea-shining,
Black licorice, long laces entwining
Shells and mussels, all manner of whorls and whirls.
I'll throw them away and keep only the pearls—

The frightened shrimps stranded in the meshing,
Pale as sand, wriggling, tail-threshing.
How many are there? Twenty, twenty-three? . . .
I'll take them home to give to the cat for tea.

Swallows in the Beach Hut

ACROSS the water under the blazing sun
The butterfly yachts are skimming;
We float in rings or go diving and swimming
Till, tired at last, we leave the waves
And over the golden sands run to our hut,
Shivering and shining-wet.

Two swallows have nested in the eaves.
They scatter and turn and plunge and pirouette,
With shrill whistlings
And much unnecessary crying fuss—
For who would wish to harm their nestlings?

Day mellows into evening; the frightened swallows
Have flown farther than the tide, their cries
Forgotten. The pools are crucibles of melted gold,
And we beside the hut, sun-drugged and old,
Bask at his fading fires and rest.
Above us, from the mud and straw of the swallows' nest
Peep three baby heads
With calm and patient and unfearing eyes.

North-Easter

I LOVE the north-easter
When it whips up the sea
And the kite on its long string
Struggles to be free.

It's blown away the gulls,
It's rattling up a gale—
Look, the yacht heels right over!
A wave grabs the sail!

A thunder-cloud above
Breaks, mumbling and grumbling;
Crowds melt away when
The rain comes tumbling.

I love it, all the wildness
I can watch from our hut,
For I'm warm and bone-dry and
The windows are shut.

'What a chance,' cry the children,
'To bathe in wind and rain!'
And they seize me by the hands and
Drag me out again.

Hares and Hounds

In autumn, chained to classrooms, we still can hear
The call of the sea. When the week is done,
We break our fetters
And down to the shore we go with scarves and sweaters,
Down to the shore, where the wind is sapping
The strength of the aged sun.
We're ready, with shouting and leaping and side-
   slapping
To play some boisterous game and run.

'Jane, what shall it be?'
Said Penelope, Anne and Helen, turning to me.
But they'd wait for no answer. 'Hares and Hounds!'
Cried Helen, with the longest legs—she's tallest.
'We'll be hares. You two can chase!'
(That's me and Andrew—he's the smallest),
And over the windy sands with leaps and bounds
Away they race.
So, while the tide was mounting,
I helped Andrew with his counting,
Till, 'Two hundred up!' he cried. 'That way
They went!' He'd squinted,
And off toward Roman Dune we sprinted.

Long before East Head we lost the trace—
No twigs or markings, no scribbled arrows.
The beach soon narrows,
And the tide clawed up the space.
No sign but a sail
Like a waving handkerchief, far out;
No sound but the muffled shout
Of sea and shingle, and the wail
Of gulls crying, 'Here!
                    here!
                         here!'

But where?
The sea had wiped out the trail,
And the rising gull-tossing gale
Was whipping the foam from the waves like froth from
  ale.

Then back with dragging steps we went,
Bad-tempered, tired and spent;
We were hounds no more, just fools and mutts.
And suddenly Andrew said, 'I know where they are!'
And pulled me through the hedge, behind the huts . . .

Those lazy hares had *not* gone far.
Those cosy-crazy hares,
Those 'wind's-too-cold-for-us-these-days'-y hares
Were huddled
           reading comics
                    in the car.

STORIES

Too Polite

Broad met Stout
At the gate, and each
Was too polite to brush past.
'After you!' said Broad.
'After you!' said Stout.
They got in a dither
And went through together
And both
       stuck
         fast.

Piano Practice

A DOTING father once there was
  Who loved his daughter Gerda,
Until she got the piano craze—
  Then how the passion stirred her!
Her fingers were wild elephants' feet,
  And as month after month he heard her
    He tried every way
    To stop her play
From bribery to murder.

One day when she was practising,
  He popped up behind and caught her
And dumped her in his wheelbarrow
  And carried her off to slaughter.
Tipping her into a well, he cried,
  'Hurrah! I've drowned my daughter!'
    But a voice from the well
    Rang out like a bell,
  'Aha—there isn't any water!'

34

Brewster Dick

(A bedtime story to keep you awake)

I THE CHASE

THIS is the tale of Brewster Dick
The Teddy Boy, who hurled a brick
In a jeweller's window, grabbed and looted
Three diamond rings, and off he shooted.
His eye was quick, his flight was dizzy,
And folk who watched him far too busy
To stop him—mothers pushing prams,
Police unsticking traffic jams.
The job of catching him was Sam's.

Trustworthy, stamped with 'Upright Stock'
Like 'Colwyn Bay' in sticks of rock,
Sam worked in T's self-service store.
While handing baskets by the score
To fretful shoppers (frightful bore),
He spied the thief and thought it right
To chase him, though he loathed a fight.

He chased him and his precious parcel
Right to Elephant and Castle,
Past movies, theatre queues and Follies,
Shops for selling fudge and lollies,
Clean through a fashionable weddin'
Attended by the Duke of Edin.
The roads, like rivers choked with ice,
Were blocked with traffic. Dick in a trice
Climbed a lorry forced to stop,
Then leapt and sprang from top to top
Of bus, removal van and tram,
Followed in hot pursuit by Sam,
Past traffic lights, police and pub-way,
Till he reached the Castle subway.
There, with one terrific bound,
He jumped into the Underground
And down the long dark tunnel booted.
Though so dangerously routed,
He neither died electrocuted
Nor tripped and fell with shrieks and squeals
On Bakerloo or Central wheels . . .
Sam caught him in the evening rush
On platform two at Shepherd's Bush.
'Police!' he cried, then through the crush,
Leaving neither name nor trace,
Slipped back to his self-service place.

2 WHAT HAPPENED AFTERWARDS

Dick, a lonely latchkey child,
Had grown up motherless and wild,
Rejected by a dimwit dad,
A drunkard who despised the lad.
Fed at school with text-book sap
And slushy pre-digested pap
And given nothing hard to bite,
He lacked a healthy appetite
And soon hatched out against society
The grudge that caused his impropriety.

The Bench bore all these facts in mind.
The chairman, Mr. Budd, was kind;
But one, Sir Maxwell Craxwell, Bart.,
Who had a granite stone for heart—
   This man alone
Was keen to skin him to the bone.
He gave his views with heat and rage
(You'll find them on the following page).

'This boy, this lout, this Brewster Dick,
Who stole the loot—he makes me sick.
The only cure for him's the stick,
    Or—better still—
I'd hunt him like the fox or deer
With shield and assagai and spear
(For him no fate is too severe)
And, breasting the brow of Shooter's Hill,
I'd shout "Halloo!" and "Whip-poor-will!"
Then leave him to the hounds to kill.'
(He might have fixed him on the wall
With other heads at Maxwell Hall—
Three musty victims of the hunt,
A bison, fox and elephunt.)
But in spite of his inbred authority,
He had to bow to the majority.

Then Budd, in tweeds and shirt of silk,
Smiled his smile of watered milk.
'You're on probation, Dick. Next time
We'll have to call your prank a crime
And you, my lad, a wicked criminal
Like Sweeney Todd or Lambert Siminal.'
    So, in short,
He let him go and cleared the court.

Now, being steeped in pop psychology,
He wrote the boy a deep apology;
To launch him on an honest course,
Enclosing from his private purse
One hundred pounds. What could be worse?

Dick promptly bought a motor bike.
'I've chose,' said he, 'the fastest mike,
And—jewellers' winders now be blowed!—
I'm goin' to break the Highway Code.'

His great delight was now to roar
Down England's strips of tarry floor
At ninety miles an hour and more,
Until he'd won for butting cars
Three broken limbs, proud battle scars,
Since mended at the State expense—
He never learned a grain of sense.
At last he crashed in a fish-shop front—
The glass and Brewster bore the brunt—
And there with bowed and blood-stained face
He took his cold and clammy place,
His bike—like him and his disgrace—
Too sick and twisted to be mended,
Whatever sum might be expended.

We'll leave him there to contemplate,
While you (if worth your while) debate
His undeserved—or fitting—fate.

The Witch's Cat

'My magic is dead,' said the witch. 'I'm astounded
That people can fly to the moon and around it.
It used to be mine and the cat's till they found it.
My broomstick is draughty, I snivel with cold
As I ride to the stars. I'm painfully old,
    And so is my cat;
    But planet-and-space-ship,
    Rocket or race-ship
Never shall part me from that.'

She wrote an advertisement, 'Witch in a fix
Willing to part with the whole bag of tricks,
Going cheap at the price at eighteen and six.'
But no one was ready to empty his coffers
For out-of-date rubbish. There weren't any offers—
    Except for the cat.
    'But planet-and-space-ship,
    Rocket or race-ship
  Never shall part me from that.'

The tears trickled fast, not a sentence she spoke
As she stamped on her broom and the brittle stick broke,
And she dumped in a dustbin her hat and her cloak,
Then clean disappeared, leaving no prints;
And no one at all has set eyes on her since
    Or her tired old cat.
    'But planet-and-space-ship,
    Rocket or race-ship
  Never shall part me from that.'

After Ever Happily

or The Princess and the Woodcutter*

AND they both lived happily ever after . . .
The wedding was held in the palace. Laughter
Rang to the roof as a loosened rafter
Crashed down and squashed the chamberlain flat—
And how the wedding guests chuckled at that!
'You, with your horny indelicate hands,
Who drop your haitches and call them 'ands,
Who cannot afford to buy her a dress,
How dare you presume to pinch our princess—
Miserable woodcutter, uncombed, unwashed!'
Were the chamberlain's words (before he was squashed).
'Take her,' said the Queen, who had a soft spot
For woodcutters. 'He's strong and he's handsome. Why
    not?'
'What rot!' said the King, but he dare not object;
The Queen wore the trousers—that's as you'd expect.

Said the chamberlain, usually meek and inscrutable,
'A princess and a woodcutter? The match is unsuitable.'
Her dog barked its welcome again and again,
As they splashed to the palace through puddles of rain.
And the princess sighed, 'Till the end of my life!'
'Darling,' said the woodcutter, 'will you be my wife?'
He knew all his days he could love no other,
So he nursed her to health with some help from his
    mother,
And lifted her, horribly hurt, from her tumble.
A woodcutter, watching, saw the horse stumble.
As she rode through the woods, a princess in her prime
On a dapple-grey horse . . . Now, to finish my rhyme,
I'll start it properly: Once upon a time—

* This is a love story from the Middle Ages. The poet obviously knew
his subject backwards.